At Night

by Liza Charlesworth

ISBN: 978-1-338-78278-3
Illustrated by Erika Lynne Jones
Copyright © 2021 by Liza Charlesworth. All rights reserved.
Published by Scholastic Inc., 557 Broadway, New York, NY 10012

10 9 8 7 6 5 4 3 2 1   68   21 22 23 24 25 26 27/0

Printed in Jiaxing, China. First printing, June 2021.

The owls come out
when it is night.
Hoot, hoot!

The bats come out
when it is night.
Flap, flap!

The worms come out
when it is night.
Wiggle, wiggle!

The mice come out
when it is night.
Squeak, squeak!

The deer come out
when it is night.
Eat, eat!

6

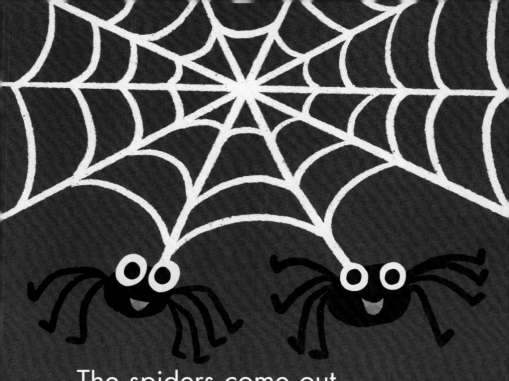

The spiders come out
when it is night.
Spin, spin!

The fireflies come out
when it is night.
Light, light!